You're obviously a talented writer, perhaps almost as good as Marvellous Me, but what would you do if you weren't an author?

That's easy — if I weren't an author I'd want to run my own second-hand bookshop. Sometimes when I can't get to sleep I imagine what the layout would be like and how I'd stock it!

If Nick wasn't your amazing illustrator, are there any other artists you admire and think could bring your characters to life?

It's very hard to imagine my books being illustrated by anyone else! There are lots of brilliant illustrators I admire — but Nick's the best.

Oh no! Pens are going to be banned and everyone will have to type on tablets! You can choose one of these to keep, which do you pick?
• A quill pen and ink bottle
• A black rollerball pen
• A swanky silver and gem-encrusted ball point

Can I cheat, and have the swanky silver and gem-encrusted pen, but a rollerball rather than a ball point?

Do you have a favourite pen to write with?

I have a slim black pen that was a special present from my daughter Emma.

What is your greatest fear?

My greatest fear is that something bad might happen to my loved ones — this is what comes of having a vivid imagination.

Your glasses are a trademark style at school for wearing them. Have you ever tried contact lenses?

I wasn't bullied by the other children at school when I first had to wear glasses — but my teacher called me Four-Eyes! He was horrible. I don't think teachers would be allowed to call children nasty nicknames nowadays. I did wear contact lenses when I was in my twenties but I was forever getting grit in them so I switched back to glasses.

Imagine you're appearing on *The Chase*, trying to win thousands for your chosen charity. Which three celeb team mates would you like take part with and why?

My celeb team mates would be Richard Osman from Pointless (he's lovely and ultra knowledgable) Claudia Winkleman (great fun) and Graham Norton (cheeky and quick-witted).

Which Chaser would you want to go up against?

Hmmm, definitely not The Governess, Anne — she's far too scary. Perhaps Paul Sinha would be best. He's very good, but he has a cheeky side to him too.

Which celebrity reality show would you like to appear on?

I wouldn't really like to appear on any of them. If I were younger I'd like to go on *Strictly*, as I love dancing.

BEST AND WORST

And now I will snoop into your deepest secrets, asking you to Reveal All!

Party you've attended...

Best: My friend Thorne's Bar Mitzvah — it went on for many hours. Thorne himself arrived on the back of the coolest motorbike while raucous rock music played — magic for a 13 year old!

Worst: A long-ago New Year's Eve party I gave myself. Can't bear to think about it!

A Bar Mitzvah is a Jewish celebration that takes place when a child turns 13!

Present you've received...

Best: A traditional full-size rocking horse — when I was an adult.

Worst: A startlingly bright turquoise mock-fur coat chosen by my mum — when I was a self-conscious teenager.

Holiday you've had...

Best: A week with a lot of writer friends in Mauritius.

Worst: A week in Wales when it rained relentlessly every single day.

Thing you've bought...

Best: A beautiful copy of Jane Eyre by Charlotte Brontë.

Worst: A dress I'd loved in the shop, but was truly terrible when I tried it on at home.

Haircut you've had...

Best: They've all been fine since I've been grown up.

Worst: When I was a teenager I'd grown my hair to my shoulders but then went to a hairdressers and asked for it all to be cut off — and they just hacked straight round so that it looked AWFUL.

Would you rather...

• Only be able to smell cheese and onions or not be able to smell at all?
Not be able to smell at all, because I hate the smell of cheese and onions!

- Be able to fly or be invisible?

I'd love to be able to fly —
it must be a fantastic feeling.

- Be a giant elephant or a tiny little dormouse?

A giant elephant. Females are in charge of the herd, and their girl children get to stay with their mothers forever.

- Only sleep when you're standing up or only eat when you're lying down?

Eat when I was lying down — so long as I could have several pillows behind my head so that I didn't choke!

- Watch Tracy Beaker re-runs every day or swim with sharks?

I'm terrified of sharks, so I suppose I'd have to suffer the Tracy Beaker re-runs. Only joking, Tracy — I'd **LOVE** to watch the re-runs.

A little list of 5 things you can see from where you're sitting

1. Many books
2. Nick's artwork on my wall
3. Piles of letters
4. A vase of flowers
5. Several old stuffed toys

Tell us something we don't know about Jacqueline Wilson...

Something you don't know about me — I have absolutely no sense of direction. I've lived in the same town nearly all my life and yet I can still get lost going to the shops!

JW MAG IS DYSLEXIA FRIENDLY!
We use the specially developed

dyslexie font.com

so each and every child can read from the same page. #ReadEqual

HELLO 2017!

1 Sunday

Start the New Year here!

Name: ....Maryan............

A photo of me on
January 1st 2017

A new thing I'll...

Learn ......football........... ☑

Try ......Basketball........... ☑

Eat ......Brocoli............ ☑

Read ......Jacqueline Wilson...... ☑

A book I always mean to read and never get round to...

Jacqueline Wilson ☑

Something I resolve NOT to do this year...

fight with my siblings.

My A1 Must-do Goal

.......listen to......
.......mum an......
.......tie the....
.... ☑

A place to visit ....Moroco..................

Best 2017 memory ....Eid..................

Best 2017 day ....26th June..................

What I did on my birthday ....Went shopping......

Check back on December 31st to see how you did!

6

JUMP-FOR-JOY JANUARY!

2 Monday

Use a crazy dream you've had to inspire a story.

Write It!

3 Tuesday

True or false: Jacky's proper title is Lady Jacqueline Wilson.

If you were a Lady, what would your life be like? Write a diary entry.

4 Wednesday

Sketch your dream house!

Will it be a mansion filled with rooms or a cosy cottage by a lake? You decide!

Draw It!

5 Thursday

Would You Rather... stand up in front of your school and sing at assembly or confess your cringiest moment in front of everyone at a JW talk?

Send the story of your cringe to *JW Mag!* jwmag@dcthomson.co.uk

6 Friday

What do you call cheese that isn't yours? Nacho cheese!

Now write a funny poem or limerick about cheese. Lol!

LOL!

7 Saturday

Have a movie and duvet day! Snuggle on the couch with some snacks and a stack of DVDs!

Do It!

Answer: False! It's Dame Jacqueline Wilson!

7

8 Sunday

Read It!

Take the number of your age, multiply it by two, and read that many pages of a book in one go!

9 Monday

Can you find all these words relating to *Queenie* in the grid?

CROWN ✓
ELSIE ✓
HOSPITAL ✓
KITTEN ✓
NAN ✓
NURSE ✓
PRINCESS ✓
QUEEN ✓

Puzzle

H	N	D	Z	P	R	E	L	P	N
O	C	W	L	C	I	T	R	P	E
S	Z	U	O	S	E	I	N	C	E
P	W	Q	L	R	N	E	Z	V	U
I	N	E	I	C	C	P	S	Z	Q
T	W	A	E	Z	R	F	H	T	P
A	Y	S	N	T	Q	I	N	W	D
L	S	N	E	T	T	I	K	P	P
D	A	C	A	N	U	R	S	E	Q
J	R	T	B	N	F	F	S	T	F

10 Tuesday

Write It!

Write about a memory from when you were young.

11 Wednesday

TRUTH: Read a page from your diary out loud

DARE: Stay as still as a statue for a whole minute – no moving allowed!

Truth or Dare!

12 Thursday

Make friendship bracelets for you and your bestie.

Do It!

13 Friday

Grab food from the kitchen and draw a still life. Why not arrange it in funny positions before you start!

Draw It!

We ♥ Hot Chocolate

What could be nicer than a mug of delicious hot choc on a cold winter's day?

14 Saturday

For one mug you'll need:

- 150ml milk
- 40ml double cream
- 25g chocolate, chopped

Place all the ingredients in a pan and bring to the boil. Whisk until all the chocolate has melted and ask an adult to help you pour into a glass or mug. Decorate with whipped cream, sprinkles and a wafer — yum!

WHY NOT?

Try these yummy flavours — just add them to the pan after the chocolate has melted!

Nice and Nutty

- 1 tbsp Nutella
- A pinch of salt (optional)

Caramel Choccy

- 1½tbsp caramel sauce

Peanut Butter Cup

- 2 tsp peanut butter

Always ask an adult to help in the kitchen.

15 Sunday

Add some fun and funky colours to this picture of BFFs Mandy and Tanya!

Colour In!

Do It!

16 Monday

Draw a picture of your favourite JW character and send it to *JW Mag*! JW Mag, 80 Kingsway East, Dundee DD4 8SL or jwmag@dcthomson.co.uk

18 Wednesday

What might your life be like when you're older? Write about it!

Write It!

17 Tuesday

Fill in the missing letter on each line to make two new words. The name of Tracy's most loyal friend will appear in the boxes!

Puzzle

S	T	O		O	N	D
C	A	P		A	G	L	E
P	O	S		A	B	L	E
T	I	M		A	R	L	Y
D	O	O		O	Y	A	L

19 Thursday

What's the best book you've read this year? Draw a poster advertising it!

Draw It!

20 Friday

Make a List...

Of the animals you love most!

Answer: Peter

BIRD FEEDER

Feed your feathered friends this winter with this easy-peasy birdfeeder!

21 Saturday

You'll need:

- An orange
- A metal spoon
- A skewer
- String
- Birdseed mix

- Cut the orange in half and scoop out the insides. Let the orange dry out a little — leave overnight if possible.

- Ask an adult to make small holes in the skin — two at each side of the base of the orange.

- Thread the string through, then tie all the loose ends together at the top. Fill with birdseed, hang up outside and watch the birds flock to feed!

Some things birds like to eat:

Fruit — especially apples!

Seeds

Nuts

Fat from bacon or other meat

Cereal crumbs

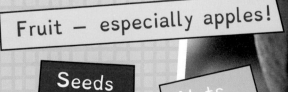

22 Sunday

Truth or Dare!

TRUTH: Confess your most secret wish

DARE: Copy everything the person nearest you does for 10 minutes!

23 Monday

Write It!

Write a story from the point of view of a nasty character! What makes them the way they are? Do they know they're horrible?

24 Tuesday

Draw It!

Transform Tremendous Tracy Beaker into a mermaid!

25 Wednesday

Do It!

Make up a new dance to your favourite song!

26 Thursday

Write It!

Think of something that made you laugh out loud and write about it.

27 Friday

Trivia Time!

What was the twins' mother's name in *Double Act*?

Now read the book!

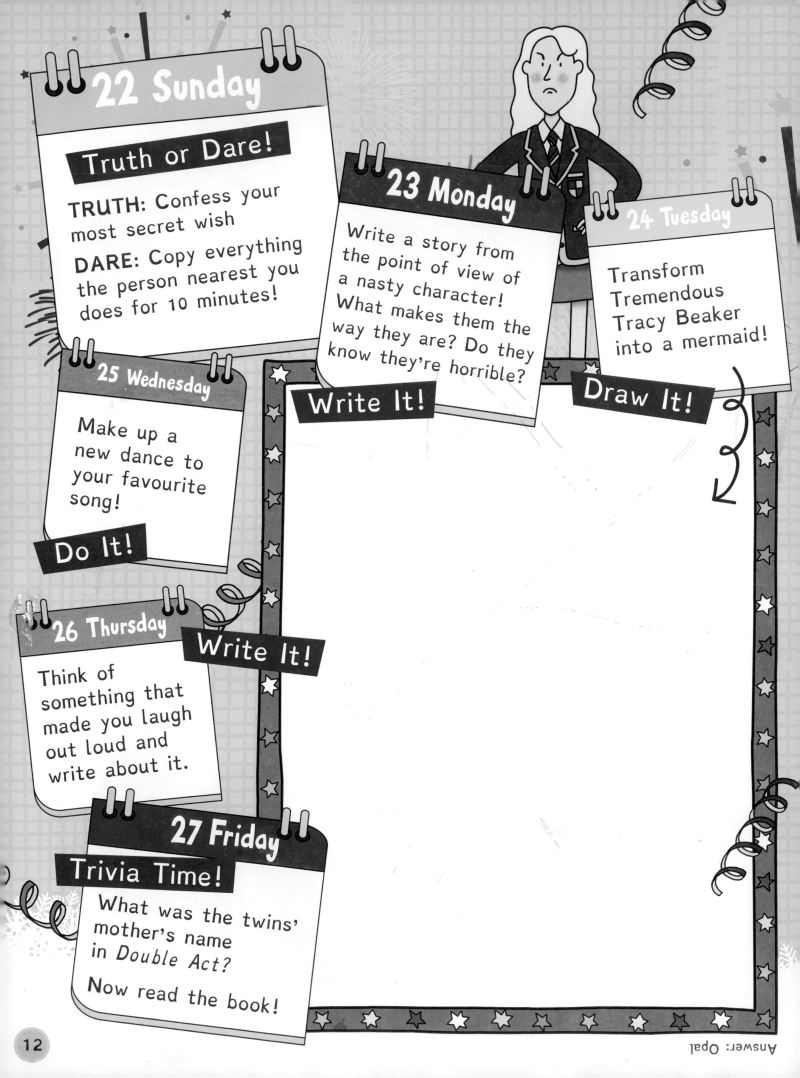

Answer: Opal

28 Saturday

Nail Art!

1. Paint your nails a base colour.
2. Add another layer of your base colour and include blobs of a contrasting colour.
3. Swirl the colours together with a toothpick and seal with clear polish.

1

2

3

29 Sunday

Susan Coolidge — Author Birthday

Jacky's book, *Katy*, is a modern re-write of *What Katy Did*, which was written in 1872 by a lady called Sarah Chauncey Woolsey. Sarah, who was born on January 29, 1835, used the pen name Susan Coolidge for her books.

What would you choose for a pen name?

....

30 Monday

Truth or Dare!

TRUTH: Answer truthfully – have you ever blabbed someone's secret?

DARE: Speak in a foreign accent for the rest of the day!

31 Tuesday

Design a beautiful new dress for Hetty!

Colour In!

FANTASTIC FEBRUARY!

DRAW IT!

1 Wednesday

Take a good look in the mirror and sketch a selfie!

PUZZLE

2 Thursday

Can you find all these characters from the Tracy Beaker books?

ADELE
CAM
ELAINE
FOOTBALL
JUSTINE
LOUISE
MIKE
PETER
TRACY
ALEXANDER

WRITE IT!

3 Friday

Write a story titled *Superstar Sisters!*

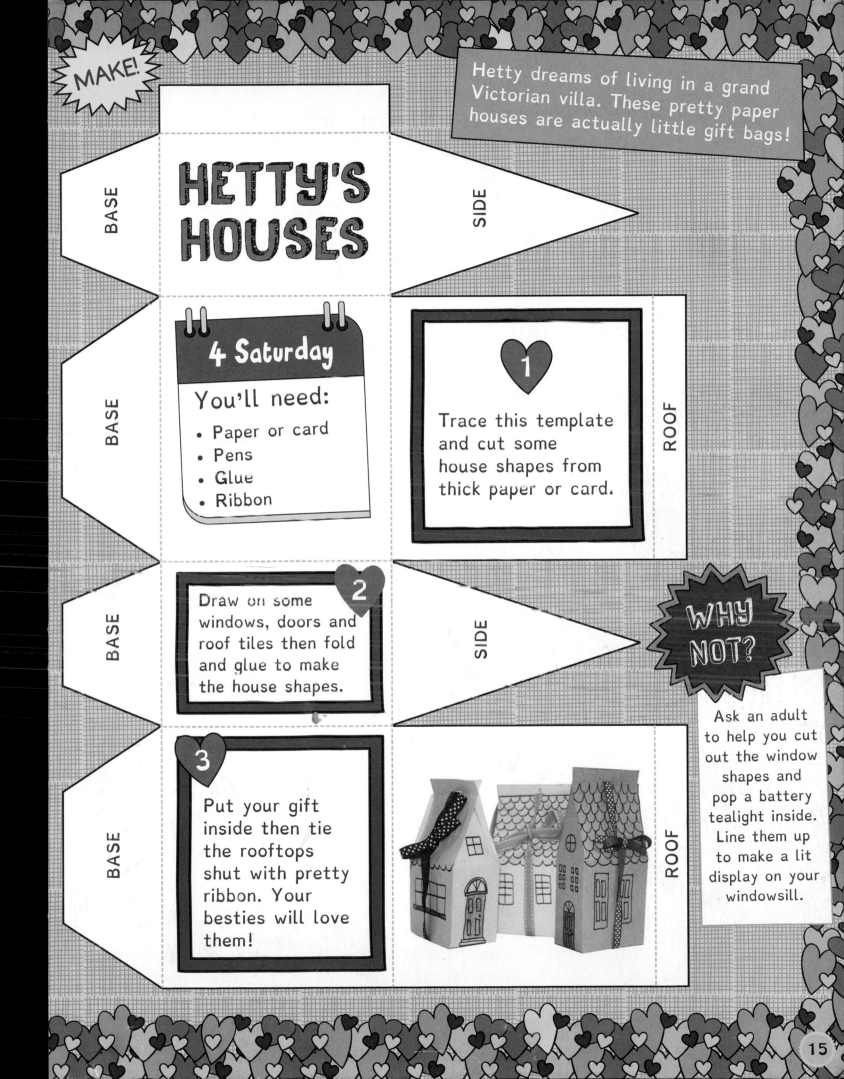

BASE

SIDE

HETTY'S HOUSES

Hetty dreams of living in a grand Victorian villa. These pretty paper houses are actually little gift bags!

4 Saturday

You'll need:
- Paper or card
- Pens
- Glue
- Ribbon

BASE

ROOF

1

Trace this template and cut some house shapes from thick paper or card.

2

Draw on some windows, doors and roof tiles then fold and glue to make the house shapes.

BASE

SIDE

WHY NOT?

3

Put your gift inside then tie the rooftops shut with pretty ribbon. Your besties will love them!

BASE

ROOF

Ask an adult to help you cut out the window shapes and pop a battery tealight inside. Line them up to make a lit display on your windowsill.

5 Sunday

TRUTH OR DARE!

TRUTH: Reveal a secret that you've never told anyone!
DARE: Run up and down your street 10 times!

6 Monday

DO IT!

Make up a spooky story to tell at your next sleepover!

7 Tuesday

Marty loves her superhero alter-ego, Mighty Mart — create one of your own and give them a fab costume!

8 Wednesday

Would you rather...

...have the head of a baby on your body or your head on a baby's body?

Draw what you might look like!

9 Thursday

LOL!

What do you get when a witch visits the seaside?
A sand-witch!

Write a story about a witch visiting the seaside!

10 Friday

PUZZLE

Cross out every letter that appears three times to reveal the name of one of Jacky's characters. Do you know which book they're from?

P	S	L	B	M	U
Z	G	M	L	C	S
R	M	B	N	L	P
S	E	C	U	B	U
T	P	Z	C	A	Z

11 Saturday

Write a letter to someone who inspires you.

12 Sunday

Write 200 words about a time you did something really exciting – remember to add lots of description to emphasise how you felt!

13 Monday

GUESS WHO!

She's got a sparkly personality, she has long, flowing hair, and she likes performing brilliant acrobatics... If you were on stage what would your act be?

Now design a poster to advertise your show!

14 Tuesday

Make these chocolates for someone you care about!

VALENTINE MAKE!

Pretty Little Choccies!

You'll need:

● A chocolate or ice cube mould (we got our mould for £1 from Asda)

○ Cake sprinkles

○ White chocolate

1 Place some cake sprinkles in the bottom of your chocolate mould – don't completely cover the bottom as the chocolate will need to get in-between the sprinkles.

2 Melt the chocolate and pour into the moulds. Use a teaspoon to help you measure out just enough for each one.

3 Leave to chill and then pop out of their cases once they've hardened – yummy!

Answer: 13 – Diamond.

DRAW IT!

15 Wednesday

Sketch your best friend's fave things and give the picture to her as a present.

WRITE IT!

16 Thursday

Flip through an old photo album until you find a funny pic — use it to inspire a story.

DO IT!

17 Friday

Have a pizza party and decorate your own pizzas like funny faces — just like the girls in *Sleepovers*!

READ IT!

18 Saturday

Open up a book you've read in the past at a random page and try to remember what's already happened up to that point.

LOL!

19 Sunday

What's brown and has a head and tail but no legs?

A penny!

If you were in charge of the country, what would money look like?

Sketch out a design for your coins and notes.

MAKE A LIST!

20 Monday

Write down your 10 favourite things ever here!

WRITE IT!

21 Tuesday

Mix it up! Imagine if Hetty met Tracy or Opal met Lily. How would they get along?

22 Wednesday

TRIVIA TIME!

In *The Story of Tracy Beaker*, who does Tracy want to get fostered by?

Imagine you live in the Dumping Ground with Tracy. Would you be friends or enemies? Write a story about your adventures!

23 Thursday

COLOUR IN!

Design a sumptuous outfit for Madame Adeline!

24 Friday

DRAW IT!

Draw a family member – Nick Sharratt style!

25 Saturday

NAIL ART!

1. Paint your nails a base colour – we chose white!
2. Drag another colour across your nail using a toothpick.
3. Repeat till you've got super-cool paint splat nails!

26 Sunday

Would You Rather...

...eat stinky cheese sandwiches for one lunch or wear stinky socks for an entire week?

Write a story that has stinky cheese and stinky socks in it!

27 Monday

Help Hetty put the coloured shapes into the matching spaces to reveal the people she's met in her travels.

F E R A
  L B
M O T N D I

1. D I A
2. F l o r a
3.

WE ♥ PANCAKES

Always ask an adult for help in the kitchen!

28 Tuesday

For basic pancakes, you'll need:

- 100g plain flour
- Pinch of salt
- 2 eggs
- 300ml semi-skimmed milk
- 1tbsp sunflower oil

- Put the flour and salt into a large mixing bowl. Crack the eggs into the middle of the flour, add the oil, then pour 50ml of milk in and whisk into a thick paste.

- Add another 50ml of milk to the paste and whisk, then steadily pour in the remaining milk as you whisk. Your batter should be like a thick cream.

- Cook in a frying pan with oil or a little butter. After 30 seconds, carefully flip your pancake over and leave for another 30 seconds.

FLAVOUR STATION

Try out these tasty toppings on Pancake Day!

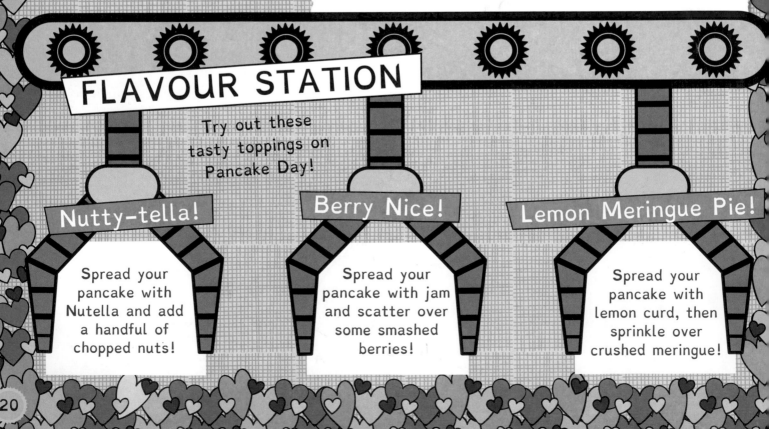

Nutty-tella!
Spread your pancake with Nutella and add a handful of chopped nuts!

Berry Nice!
Spread your pancake with jam and scatter over some smashed berries!

Lemon Meringue Pie!
Spread your pancake with lemon curd, then sprinkle over crushed meringue!

MARVELLOUS MARCH!

WRITE IT!

1 Wednesday

Imagine if you were to interview Jacqueline Wilson for *JW Mag* — what questions would you ask her?
Write them down!

TRUTH OR DARE!

2 Thursday

TRUTH: If you found £10 in the street, what would you do with it?

DARE: Do your silliest dance moves in front of everyone!

WRITE IT!

3 Friday

Create a character that you'd love to have as a best friend! Maybe they'll be just like you or it'll be a case of opposites attract! Write lots of descriptive paragraphs about what they look like, too! Maybe they're glamorous and exotic, or eccentric and fun!

DRAW IT!

4 Saturday

A mountain scene using lots of gorgeous colours for the beautiful surroundings!

5 Sunday

Go on a nature walk in the woods — what will you see?

DO IT!

6 Monday

Would you rather...
...crawl like a baby to get everywhere or only be able to walk backwards? Choose a book at random and read the end. Now try to write a start for it!

COLOUR IN!

LOL!

8 Wednesday

What stays in the corner but travels all over the world?

A stamp!

Design a stamp with your head on it!

9 Thursday

Imagine if you could change into any creature you liked — what adventures would you have?

WRITE IT!

7 Tuesday

Can you give Jacky a fancy new look?

10 Friday

Take a selfie then use a photo or art app to change your hairstyles!

DO IT!

PRETTY PAPER FLOWERS

I'm making Marigold lots of these for Mother's Day!

1. Place four sheets of tissue paper on top of each other, fold in half and cut into two along the fold line. Fold each paper pile in half again.

Draw two circles on to each top layer (a CD is the perfect size for this) and cut out. You should now have eight sets of circles with four layers in each set.

11 Saturday

You'll need:
• Tissue paper
• Scissors
• Stapler

Gorgeous!

2. Fold each circle set into four and draw on a heart shape like this.

Cut round the top edge

3. Gather all the flower shapes together (there should be 32 layers altogether) and staple through the centre.

4. Starting on top, fluff up one layer at a time like this.

Keep going till you've fluffed up all the layers and your flowers look finished.

WHY NOT?

• Add some chenille craft stick stems to create a beautiful bouquet.

• Draw round a glass to make smaller flowers and glue them to a plain hairband for a stunning floral crown.

23

12 Sunday

You have 10 minutes to find 10 words connected to *The Illustrated Mum!*

Marigold
Dolphin
Star
Tattoos
Brighton
Scarf
Sorceress
Owly
Angel
Badges

R	F	N	Y	Y	Q	Z	I	S	Z
N	A	O	E	A	M	S	S	C	P
T	I	T	H	N	A	E	I	A	K
A	E	H	S	G	R	U	E	R	U
T	O	G	P	E	I	M	C	F	L
T	L	I	C	L	G	L	S	L	F
O	T	R	V	B	O	D	T	I	X
O	O	B	T	W	H	D	A	E	Y
S	P	K	L	G	D	T	M	B	B
R	W	Y	H	I	W	H	D	T	Z

WRITE IT!

13 Monday

Write a story without using the word 'and' — it's tricky, so well done if you manage!

WRITE IT!

14 Tuesday

Pick a favourite story from your childhood and re-write it, just like Jacky did for *Katy* and *Four Children and It!*

COLOUR IN!

15 Wednesday

Add some colour to this picture of Gemma and Alice!

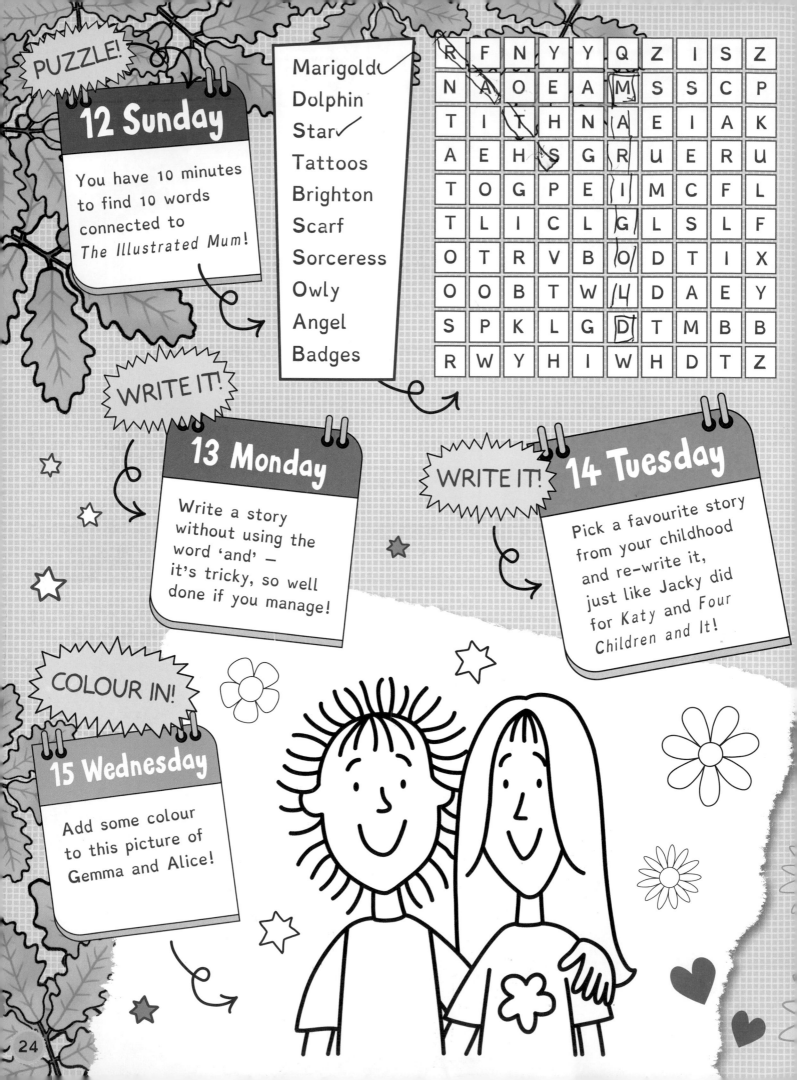

DRAW IT!

16 Thursday

Fold your paper into quarters and sketch the same tree in all four seasons.

17 Friday

Would you rather...
...live in a spooky graveyard with your family or all alone on a desert island?

Imagine you do live in a graveyard. Are you alive or a ghost? Write about it.

DO IT!

18 Saturday

Give your bedroom a makeover (or just a tidy if you're super-messy!)

MAKE A LIST...

19 Sunday

Write your top five favourite possessions here...

1. _____
2. _____
3. _____
4. _____
5. _____

TRUTH OR DARE!

20 Monday

TRUTH: What's your most embarrassing moment?

DARE: Eat a chocolate biscuit covered in ketchup!

DRAW IT!

21 Tuesday

Draw an outline of your name then fill each letter with different patterns.

22 Wednesday

Cross out every second letter to discover which book has a character that lives with her dad!

CBAGNUDIYFFPLUOASMS

READ IT!

23 Thursday

Read for 20 minutes every evening for the next week!

Ballet Shoes by Noel Streatfeild

The Children From One End Street by Eve Garnet

The Railway Children by E Nesbit

Little Women by Louisa M Alcott

A Little Princess by Frances Hodgson Burnett

What Katy Did by Susan Coolidge

Mary Poppins by P L Travers

Marianne Dreams by Catherine Storr

The Diary of Anne Frank by Anne Frank

I Capture The Castle by Dodie Smith

WRITE IT!

24 Friday

Be a song-writer! Pick your fave piece of music and write new lyrics to fit the tune.

NAIL ART!

25 Saturday

1. Paint your nails a punchy spring colour — we chose a sunny yellow shade.

2. Use a contrast colour and a toothpick with the pointy ends cut off to add five dots that meet in the middle.

3. Use the toothpick to add a dot of the original colour in the middle — done!

GUESS WHO!

26 Sunday

She has a fierce temper and gets into trouble a lot. She hates her dad's girlfriend and someone in her life looks like her...

Have you ever had a temper tantrum? Draw a raging picture of yourself!

DRAW IT!

27 Monday

Design a delicious-looking birthday cake!

TRIVIA TIME!

28 Tuesday

In *Best Friends*, where does Alice move to?

If your BF moved away, how would you feel? Write a diary entry about it.

COLOUR IN!

29 Wednesday

Colour these pretty flowers your way!

WRITE IT!

30 Thursday

Write a story about a girl that can talk to the creatures in her garden.

LOL!

31 Friday

What did the pencil say to the other pencil? You're looking sharp!

Make up your own 'What did' joke!

Awesome April!

1 Saturday
DO IT! Pretend you're a YouTuber, and describe what's in your bag — you don't have to film it, it's just for fun!

2 Sunday
Can you rearrange these letters to make up a JW book title?

MESSY RIDE JOT I

----

3 Monday
Would you rather...
never write again
OR
never watch TV again?
Write a review of your fave TV show!

4 Tuesday
WRITE IT! Look out of the window and pick five things that you see. Now write a story that links them together!

5 Wednesday
COLOUR IN! Add a splash of colour to this picture of Tina. Give her top a fab pattern!

DRAW IT!
6 Thursday

Trace the cover of your favourite JW book, then colour it in your way!

7 Friday

TRUTH:
If you were stuck on a desert island, which friend would you want there with you and why?

DARE:
Talk to a stuffed animal like it's your BFF for the rest of the game!

8 Saturday

WRITE IT!

Write a story about you and your friends where your characters are totally opposite to what they are now!

DO IT!
9 Sunday

Watch an old black and white film — ask your grandparents to recommend one!

One of Jacky's favourite old films is **Mandy** — Jacky once also met the film's star, Mandy Miller!

10 Monday

GUESS WHO?
She loves superheroes, she's not a fan of dresses, she doesn't get on with her sister...
Make up your own superhero comic strip!

11 Tuesday

Get creative with your pens and colour in this picture of Ruby and Garnet! Will you make them match or clash?

COLOUR IN!

12 Wednesday

How quickly can you find all these words that are connected to *My Sister Jodie*?
Melchester ★ Pearl ★ Tower ★ Jodie
Fireworks ★ Badgers ★ Harley
Party ★ Ghost ★ Red shoes

M	E	G	O	V	O	B	I	R	T
I	E	G	U	L	R	A	E	P	X
L	K	D	A	L	E	D	C	N	M
T	S	Z	G	H	S	G	N	Y	T
T	N	L	X	A	E	T	P	K	K
S	K	R	O	W	E	R	I	F	Y
O	D	E	A	I	A	S	L	C	E
H	S	W	D	P	P	D	T	E	J
G	Q	O	P	M	S	R	K	E	Y
K	J	T	C	G	W	U	B	N	R

WRITE IT!
13 Thursday

Write about the life of a girl who's just like you... but lives on the other side of the world! What's the weather like, what does she eat, and where does she live?

Daisy's Easter Pizza

Make a yummy custom pizza like mine!

YOU'LL NEED:

- Pizza base mix
- Selection of vegetables
- Red pesto sauce or pizza topping sauce
- Grated cheese

Always ask an adult for help in the kitchen.

1. Follow the packet instructions to make up the pizza base then roll out on a floured surface.

2. Trace this egg template and cut a pattern from paper. Now use the pattern to cut out the egg shape from your dough. Place the dough egg on a prepared baking tray.

3. Spread on the pesto or pizza sauce and a light layer of cheese. Now arrange chopped up veggies to make your own awesome Easter egg design. Sprinkle with some more cheese.

4. Follow the packet instructions to bake your pizza, then enjoy!

SPRING THINGS!

15 Saturday

YOU'LL NEED:
- Polystyrene eggs
- Wooden skewers
- School glue
- Cake sprinkles
- Ribbon
- Glitter or sparkly shapes

1 Carefully push the skewers into the polystyrene eggs.

2 Mix together the sprinkles, glitter and sparkly shapes in a shallow dish.

3 Coat the eggs in glue, then roll in sprinkles. Leave to dry.

4 Tie a ribbon underneath each egg and arrange in a vase.

Make this cute spring table decoration!

31

DO IT!

16 Sunday

EASTER EGG NAILS!

Your nails will look good enough to eat!

1. Paint your nails a base colour — we went for lots of different pastel shades!

2. Use toothpicks to add detail in a contrasting colour. If you cut a toothpick in half, you can make dots with the blunt end. The pointy end is great for stripes!

3. Finish with a topcoat and admire your beautiful new nails!

20 Thursday

Where does Jacky live?

Draw a map of your home town.

FACT OR FICTION?

21 Friday

Which of these JW facts are totally true — and which are porky pies?

	TRUE	FALSE
Marty's real name is Martina	✓	✓
Justine broke Tracy's Mickey Mouse clock	✓	✓
Opal Plumstead is fourteen years old	✓	✓
Garnet wins a scholarship to attend Marnock Heights	✓	✓
Biscuits real name is Timmy	✓	✓

DOODLE & DESIGN!

18 Tuesday

17 Monday
WRITE IT!
Imagine waking up one morning to discover you're in someone else's body! Now write about it!

Add some cute 'n' colourful designs to these Easter eggs!

19 Wednesday
WOULD YOU RATHER?
Have fingers as long as legs or legs as long as fingers? Draw a sketch of your choice!

DRAW IT!
22 Saturday
Create textures in your sketchbook — copy the weave of fabric, strands of hair in a plait or the shiny surface of a plate!

23 Sunday
READ IT!
Try to finish a new book in one week!

24 Monday
What did one firefly say to the other? You glow, girl!

LOL!

How many words can you think of that rhyme with glow?

25 Tuesday
WRITE IT!
Write a story where you start every sentence with a word beginning with the first letter of your name!

33

26 Wednesday

How many words of three letters or more can you make out of this book title?

THE LONGEST WHALE SONG

1-5   Grab your dictionary and try again!

6-10 Well done!

11+   Your vocabulary rules!

27 Thursday

TRUTH:
Share your scariest ever moment

DARE:
Wear socks on your hands for the next hour!

DO IT!
28 Friday

Create your own flavour of milkshake using your favourite tastes — banana and peanut butter is super-yummy!

yum!

29 Saturday

DRAW IT! See if your pet will sit still long enough for you to draw them!

30 Sunday

Colour in this picture of Lily staring out of the window. What is she looking at outside? Why not use this picture to inspire your next story?

COLOUR IN!

MAGNIFICENT MAY!

Fill in the grid!

1 Monday

Fit these words in the grid to discover where Tracy wants to end up!

RADIANT
GLOW
FASHION
GLORY
FAMOUS
STARLET
STYLE
OSCAR
ACTOR

2 Tuesday

DO IT.

Grab a pack of cards and play Snap with your family!

3 Wednesday

COLOUR IN!

Give Nick a fancy new outfit!

4 Thursday

DRAW IT.

Draw your BFFs and give them your sketches as a gift!

5 Friday

WRITE IT!

Create a character that you'd love to have as a best friend!

Answer: Hollywood

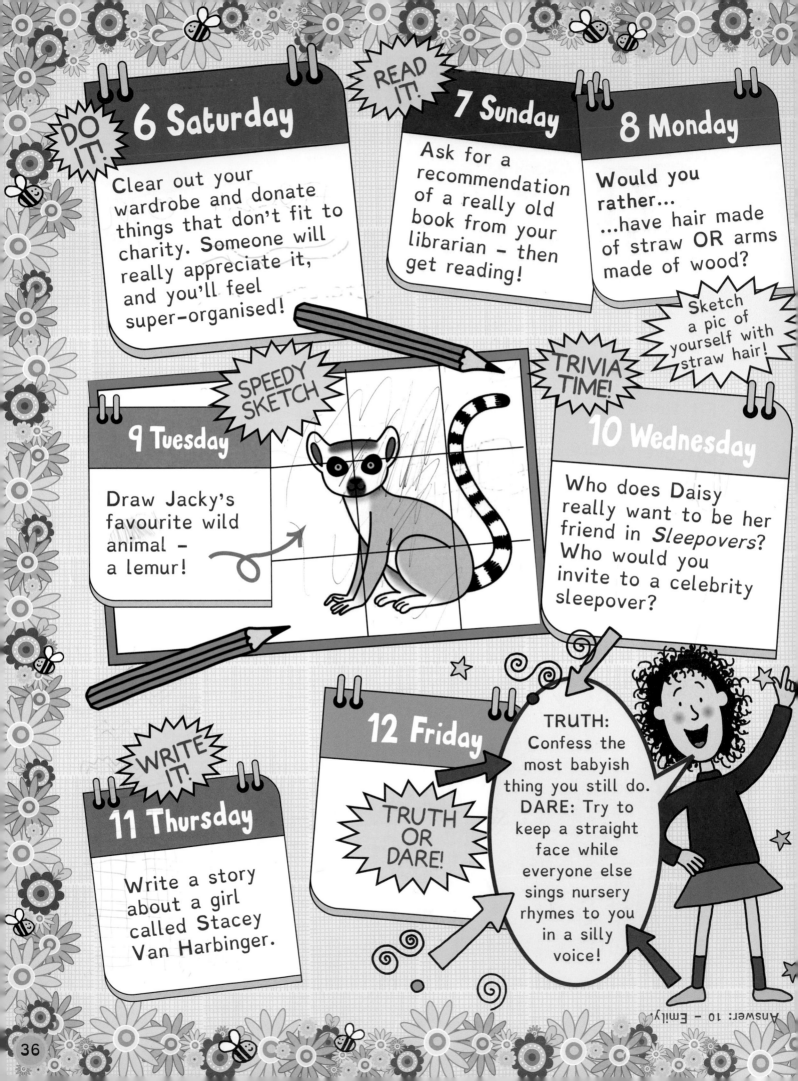

DO IT!

6 Saturday

Clear out your wardrobe and donate things that don't fit to charity. Someone will really appreciate it, and you'll feel super-organised!

READ IT!

7 Sunday

Ask for a recommendation of a really old book from your librarian – then get reading!

8 Monday

Would you rather... ...have hair made of straw OR arms made of wood?

Sketch a pic of yourself with straw hair!

SPEEDY SKETCH

9 Tuesday

Draw Jacky's favourite wild animal – a lemur!

TRIVIA TIME!

10 Wednesday

Who does Daisy really want to be her friend in *Sleepovers*? Who would you invite to a celebrity sleepover?

WRITE IT!

11 Thursday

Write a story about a girl called Stacey Van Harbinger.

12 Friday

TRUTH OR DARE!

TRUTH: Confess the most babyish thing you still do. DARE: Try to keep a straight face while everyone else sings nursery rhymes to you in a silly voice!

Answer: 10 – Emily.

13 Saturday

You'll need:

- Cupcakes (buy ready made or use our recipe on page 52)
- Icing
- Marshmallows
- Jelly sweets
- Sugar
- Food colouring

PRETTY PETAL CUPCAKES!

These cute cupcakes are so easy to make!

Make buttercream icing!

Put 340g icing sugar and 170g of soft butter or margarine in a bowl and mix together until soft and fluffy. If you don't have a mixer, start mashing with a fork, then finish beating with a wooden spoon.

Make Coloured Sugar!

Mix a few drops of food colouring with granulated sugar and stir until... it changes colour!

LET'S DECORATE:

1 Snip marshmallows into discs like this this, then dip the cut edges in the coloured sugar

2 Place a yellow jelly sweet or some jelly beans in the centre of the cupcake then arrange the marshmallow petals around the edge — cute!

14 Sunday

Oh, no! Andy from *The Suitcase Kid* has left behind her most treasured possession during her move. Can you work it out from the clues?

My first is in car but not in cat,
My second is the middle of blade.
My third is the first in deer,
My fourth is the third in while,
My fifth is in starlet but not in tartlet.
My last is the first in home.

15 Monday

Would you rather...

...live at the South Pole or in the middle of the Sahara desert?

Write a story about the place you choose!

WRITE IT!

Incorporate this character into your own story:

16 Tuesday

Blythe is the girl everyone wants to be. She's beautiful, intelligent, and radiates kindness and warmth. But she has a dark secret...

Sketch an elephant!

17 Wednesday

Speedy sketch

GUESS WHO?

18 Thursday

She has a singing half-sister who doesn't live with her. She is shy, but the rest of her family aren't!

Write a song about your family.

DRAW IT!

19 Friday

Look out of your bedroom window and draw your view. Then draw your dream view!

20 Saturday

Learn the dance routine to your favourite pop song! All you need to do is watch the video on YouTube... about 100 times!

Answers: 14 – Radish; 18 – Sunset.

38

FANCY FLOWER WALL HANGER

You'll need:

- Card
- Cardboard tubes
- Glue
- Paint
- Glitter
- Ribbon

Upcycle old cardboard tubes to make this pretty wall hanging!

1 Cut the tubes into sections, then snip down to make petals.

2 Paint the cardboard flowers and leave to dry.

3 Stick to a piece of green card and add leaf shapes to decorate. Pierce holes in the card and add some ribbon to hang — lovely!

TIP!
Sprinkle on glitter when the paint is wet for sparkle and shine!

22 Monday

Jazz up this picture of Tracy and Cam. What are they celebrating? It's up to you!

23 Tuesday

Q. How do trees get on to the internet?
A. They log on!

Tell this joke to everyone you meet today!

24 Wednesday

Draw round your hand and then decorate it with elaborate jewellery and nail art!

25 Thursday

What colour is Mandy's hair in *Bad Girls*?

Now try drawing her a brand new hair do!

26 Friday

Write a story called *The Incredible Tale Of Mr Itch*!

Answer: 25 – Blonde

27 Saturday

NAIL ART!

1. Paint your nails a base colour.
2. Use a sponge to dab on a contrasting colour. Start halfway down the nail, then add extra polish to the tip.
3. Add a glitter top coat to an accent nail for extra sparkle!

1 2 3

28 Sunday

WRITE IT!

Can you write a short story by bedtime today?

30 Tuesday

MAKE A LIST!

Write ten things you REALLY HATE here:

....
....
....
....
....
....
....
....
....

29 Monday

Would You Rather...

...have back-to-back maths lessons all day, or have to do one maths problem on stage at assembly?

Write a story about one or the other.

31 Wednesday

WRITE IT!

Write about an old man who doesn't have any friends or family left... until one day he meets someone very special!

JUST-DO-IT

1 Thursday

WRITE IT!

The setting: You're dreaming and you're in a land where everything is soft and squishy — even the pavements are springy like bouncy castles.

Next, fill in this list of your favourites —

Food: _Pizza_

Colour: _gold_

TV show: _Disney Channel_

Song: _____

Place: _____

Shop: _____

Now write a story set in your dream land that includes all your favourite things!

2 Friday

WRITE IT!

You're out for a walk and you find a large green egg lying on the path. When you touch it, it feels warm, so you wrap it safely in your jumper and take it home. You put the egg in a cosy place and keep it safe. Then one day you hear a tap, tap, tapping — the egg is hatching! You hold your breath as the shell breaks open to reveal...

???

What's inside your egg? A fancy bird? A baby dragon? A tiny person? The rest is up to you!

3 Saturday

WRITE IT!

Look at this picture and write a story inspired by it. Who are the people? Why have they gone out for tea? Has something cringing just happened? You decide!

JUNE!

WEEK OF WRITING!

4 Sunday

Ever read a book you didn't like? Rearrange the characters and ideas to create a brand new story you'd love!

5 Monday

Have you ever told a big fat fib? Write a story about what happens when someone tells a lie.

6 Tuesday

You're given a magic wand to look after, but can you resist the temptation to try it out? What happens if you do? Maybe the wand is stolen from you!

7 Wednesday

If your favourite toys could talk what would they be saying? Imagine Jacky's Victorian dolls chatting about fashion!

8 Thursday

Ouch! Think of a time you hurt yourself and write about it. Use lots of description so everyone can share your pain!

9 Friday

Imagine you're building your dream house. It will have exactly the things you want. Describe what it looks like and everything in it.

10 Saturday

Write about a TV advert that really, really, really annoys you! Why do you dislike it so much? How does it make you feel?

I'll have fluffy white carpets and a humungous TV!

DO IT!

11 Sunday

Decide on a new skill or talent to learn over the summer holidays.
Keep track of your progress along the way — you'll feel great when you've done it!

12 Monday

Would you rather...
...wear your clothes back-to-front or your shoes on the wrong feet all day? Sketch your favourite shoes!

MAKE A LIST...

14 Wednesday

Write down your 5 favourite songs ever!

DRAW IT!

13 Tuesday

Can you fill a page of your sketchbook with teeny-tiny doodles?

COLOUR IN!

15 Thursday

Colour in this picture of young Jacky tucking into her favourite cakes!

WRITE IT!

16 Friday

Write a story about a team of superhero farm animals — and that includes making up funny names for them!

CUTE OWL CARD!

Perfect for Father's Day!

17 Saturday

You'll need:
• Brown card
• Orange and white foam or card
• Glue
• A pen

• Cut out these shapes — use brown card for the body and wings, orange foam for the belly and a beak, and white foam for the eyes.

• Glue everything down as shown. Once the glue has dried, fold the wings back and write a message on the owl's belly. Add detail to the eyes and wings to finish. Cute!

DAD, YOU'RE A HOOT!
♥ FLOSS x

MAKE IT!

18 Sunday

DOUGHNUT DELIGHTS!

Grab a box of plain doughnuts and jazz them up with these delicious toppings!

- Make plain water icing by mixing a few teaspoons of water with icing sugar till it's thick enough to coat a spoon.
- Make chocolate icing by adding in some cocoa powder.
- Just dunk your doughnuts into the icing to quickly coat the tops — easy!

Awesome Orange!

- Swap water for orange juice and orange food colouring in the icing mix. Dunk the doughnut and finish with orange sprinkles.

Berry Bite!

- Crush and sieve some summer berries to get the juice. Add this to plain icing and dunk your doughnut.
- When it's dry, decorate with a drizzle of plain white icing.

Salted Caramel Supreme!

- Add a tablespoon of caramel sauce and a pinch of salt to plain icing.
- Cover the doughnut with caramel mix then drizzle on lines of chocolate icing. Drag a toothpick through the lines to get a cool pattern!

Lovely Lemon!

- Add lemon juice and yellow food colouring to plain icing.
- Cover the doughnut and leave to dry. Decorate with another drizzle of icing.

Peppermint Punch!

- Add a couple of drops of peppermint extract and green food colouring to plain icing, then top with green sprinkles. Nom!

19 Monday

Can you read (or re-read!) all the *Hetty Feather* books before the end of the summer?

Jacqueline Wilson
HETTY FEATHER
ILLUSTRATED BY NICK SHARRATT

TRUE OR FALSE?

20 Tuesday

The Worst Thing About My Sister was inspired by Jacky's childhood. Write your own version of the book — will you be Marty or Melissa?

WRITE IT!

21 Wednesday

Write about a time you felt really scared — remember to add lots of drama and description to your story!

GUESS WHO!

22 Thursday

She loves school, but has to leave to help her family earn money. She has a gemstone first name.
List the best things about your school.

PUZZLE!

23 Friday

Solve this secret code to discover Katy's favourite hiding place!

SYMBOL KEY

A=🧁 B=⭐ C=🥬 D=🍒 E=🦋 F=🌸 G=🌞
H=✴ I=🎾 J=🐝 K=⚽ L=🥤 M=🦋 N=🐟
O=🌈 P=🍌 Q=🍉 R=👟 S=🐌 T=🌼 U=🍫
V=🍍 W=⭐ X=🍎 Y=🐞 Z=🌻

T H E

S E C R E T

G A R D E N

46

24 Saturday

Ask an adult to help you cut some potatoes into shapes, then make a cool pattern using bold poster paints!

DO IT!

25 Sunday

SPEEDY SKETCH!

Draw a Sharratt parrot!

TRIVIA TIME!

26 Monday

Which book was Jacky's 100th?

Design a cover for it your way!

? ? ?

27 Tuesday

Would you rather... ...only be able to talk backwards or never talk at all?

Learn to count to 10 in a new language!

DRAW IT!

28 Wednesday

Draw a slice of the most delicious pizza you can imagine! Add all your fave toppings!

Answers:
20 — False! Jacky was inspired by one of her friend's childhood anecdotes of sharing a room with her sister; 22 — Opal Plumstead; 23 — The Secret Garden; 26 — Opal Plumstead.

29 Thursday

Pick your three favourite JW characters and write them into a story together. Will they all get on with each other?

30 Friday

Be a fashion designer and create a fabulous outfit and accessories for yourself!

SavageLife

MK

JOYOUS JULY!

MELISSA'S GORGEOUS GLITTER BOWLS

1 Saturday

You'll need:

- Glitter
- School glue
- Balloons
- Paint brush

1 Pour some school glue into a plastic tub and add a generous dollop of glitter. Mix together using the brush.

2 Blow up a balloon to the size you want and put in a bowl or plant pot to keep it steady. Now paint on a thick layer of the glitter glue — it doesn't matter if it starts to run.

3 Leave to dry then add another coat. Keep adding glitter glue layers until it's as sparkly as you'd like — we did three coats.

TIP!
Spray the outside of the bowl with hairspray to stop glitter shedding off.

4 Leave to dry thoroughly — overnight is best. Now burst the balloon and gently peel it away from the glittery shell. Trim away any drips or runs and you're left with a sparkling bowl.

The perfect place to keep all your sparkling treasures and accessories!

2 Sunday

Make a List

Write down everything you want to do this summer!

3 Monday

Which JW book starts with the lines: *I lived with my nan. It was wonderful, just the two of us, in our cosy basement flat?*

Now use these opening lines to start a story!

Trivia Time!

4 Tuesday

You're taking a nice stroll through a forest when you come across a door in a huge tree... What's on the other side? It's up to you!

Write It!

5 Wednesday

Guess Who?

Her parents have split up and she has to share her time with them and their new families. She has a lucky rabbit mascot called **Radish**.

Can you find Radish hiding on this page?

6 Thursday

Can you read a chapter of your book every night this week before you go to bed?

Read It!

7 Friday

Create a collage using scraps of magazines, fabric and anything else you can find. Hang it in your bedroom when you're finished!

Draw It!

8 Saturday

Create your own magazine! Ask your friends if they want to help, and give everyone a job to do. You'll need an editor, writers and designers!

Do It!

9 Sunday

Pick 5 words at random from the dictionary, then include them in a 50-word story!

Write It!

50

10 Monday

Would You Rather...

...stand up and speak in front of your class or have to show everyone how to do a cartwheel in P.E.?

Write an acrostic poem using the word CARTWHEEL.

11 Tuesday

What do you call a mountain doing stand-up comedy? Hill-arious!

Write a five-minute stand-up routine!

LOL!

12 Wednesday

You have the power to grant someone a wish. Imagine what people would ask you to make come true – and how would you decide whose wish to grant?

Write It!

13 Thursday

Draw round a plate and then draw on a mouth-watering meal! Make it look as real as possible!

Draw It!

14 Friday

Give this carousel a splash of colour!

Colour In!

STRAWBERRY SENSATION!

Bake It!

You'll need:
- Two plain sponge cakes — use ready-made or our cut & keep recipe
- Fresh strawberries cut into halves
- Strawberry jam
- Fresh whipped cream or your favourite vanilla frosting
- Caster sugar

Place one sponge on a plate and spread with a thin layer of strawberry jam.

Now top with generous layer of cream or frosting. Arrange the strawberry halves neatly round the edge of the cake, then fill in the centre.

Pop on the top sponge layer and sprinkle with caster sugar. Decorate the top with a little flower of strawberry halves — stick each one on with a dab of jam or frosting. Ta-dah!

Cake + strawberries = total yum and will impress everyone with its Exquisite Grandeur!

Cut & Keep Vanilla Sponge Recipe

Makes two sponge cakes or around 20 cupcakes.

1 Place **4 large eggs** in a bowl and add **225g of caster sugar**, **225g of self-raising flour**, **2 teaspoons of baking powder**, **1 teaspoon of vanilla essence** and **225g softened butter or margarine**.

2 Whizz together with a mixer or beat with a wooden spoon until everything is well combined. Don't over-mix – the batter should be fluffy, pale yellow and drop easily off a spoon.

2 Bake at 180°C/350°F/ Gas mark 4 for 20–25 minutes for big sponges or around 15 minutes for little cakes. They're ready when they're golden brown and springy to the touch.

Always ask an adult to help in the kitchen.

16 Sunday

Nail Art!

1. Paint your nails a pretty sky blue.
2. Use a piece of sponge to dab on white for clouds
3. Paint a rainbow on your biggest fingernail — cute!

17 Monday

In *Sleepovers*, how many girls are in the Alphabet Club?

Come up with a name for your own club!

Trivia Time!

18 Tuesday

Work on a joint art project with a sibling or friend — teaming up means twice the skills and talent!

Puzzle

19 Wednesday

MARVELLOUS
TREMENDOUS
AWESOME
GOLD STAR
BRILLIANT
FANTASTIC
STUPENDOUS
TALENTED
AMAZING
SPECTACULAR

These words perfectly describe ME — can you find them all?

20 Thursday

Use a camera or your phone to take lovely pictures of your family and friends. Print them out so you can display them, or keep them in your purse.

Do It!

Draw It!

21 Friday

Did you know man landed on the moon on July 21, 1969? Write a story about Tracy B becoming the first child in space! How would she react to being picked for such a prestigious honour?

Write It!

22 Saturday

Would You Rather...

...meet a magical unicorn who would give you rides on its back or a magical wish-granting psammead?

Write down your three biggest wishes.

O	E	M	T	S	G	T	S	I	O
E	F	B	O	P	O	A	U	S	B
M	A	R	V	E	L	L	I	O	U	S
O	N	I	G	C	D	E	D	O	Z
S	T	L	N	T	S	N	N	D	E
E	A	L	I	A	T	T	E	N	F
W	S	I	Z	C	A	E	M	E	A
A	T	A	A	U	R	D	E	P	R
S	I	N	M	L	B	G	R	U	W
J	C	T	A	A	Q	E	T	T	Q
P	E	Z	C	R	R	U	W	S	O

23 Sunday

Design your dream ice cream sundae here! What flavours will you choose?

Doodle and Design!

24 Monday
Truth or Dare!

TRUTH:
Have you ever been told off for something super-embarrassing?

DARE:
Do your fanciest ballet dance in front of everyone!

25 Tuesday

Would You Rather...
...your clothes were all black or everything was vivid rainbow shades?

Design yourself a new pair of shoes in your fave colour.

26 Wednesday

You wake up to find you're a penguin at the zoo! How do you alert your keeper to this terrible mishap?

Write It!

27 Thursday
Trivia Time!

What's the name of Alice's new friend in *Best Friends*?

Write about two new BFFs meeting for the first time.

28 Friday

She has blonde hair and two step-brothers. When things change in her life, she stops speaking at all! See how long you can last without speaking!

29 Saturday

Rewrite your favourite song to make it sound super-silly! Bonus points if you perform it in front of anyone!

Do It!

30 Sunday

Draw your reflection in a shiny object like a soup spoon or the side of a toaster!

Draw It!

31 Monday

Author Birthday

JK Rowling

JK Rowling, who wrote the *Harry Potter* books, was born on July 31, 1965. She and Jacky were both lucky enough to attend the Queen's 80th birthday party at Buckingham Palace, where this picture was taken!

Write about what you think happened on the day!

Amazing August!

1 Tuesday

DOODLE & DESIGN!

Some JW characters have lucky mascots — why not give them a new look?

2 Wednesday

WRITE IT!

Write a story with the title: *The Best Friend I Never Had*

3 Thursday

TRIVIA TIME!

Who spends the summer at Evergreen Summer Camp? What would be your dream summer camp?

4 Friday

DRAW IT! Draw a picture of YOU floating in outer space!

5 Saturday

MAKE IT!

Brilliant Beach Bag!

Make a super-cute beach tote in minutes!

YOU'LL NEED:
- An old vest top
- Needle and thread
- Ribbon scraps, brooches or badges

1. Turn the vest inside out. Use a double thickness of strong thread to stitch a line of small running stitches across the bottom, just above the hem.

2. Pull the stitches tight then pass the needle through the edge of the fabric a few times to make a secure knot.

3. Turn the right way out. You now have a beach-perfect bag! Decorate it with some pretty ribbons and badges, pop in your stuff and head for the sea!

GUESS WHO?

6 Sunday

This character has a poorly mum and a younger brother who she has to help take care of. She really likes a particular type of sea creature, too! Sketch your favourite sea animal!

7 Monday

TRUTH OR DARE!

TRUTH:
Tell everyone about the time you got the biggest telling-off!

DARE:
Do a silly dance with no music for a whole minute!

8 Tuesday
WRITE IT!
Use this opening line to write whatever you like: It was a Tuesday. Tuesdays are always boring, and I decided I'd had enough!

9 Wednesday
HAPPY BIRTHDAY, NICK!
Nick Sharratt was born on August 9, 1962. He's illustrated over 250 books — some of his own and some for other authors, like Jacky. Nick has been illustrating Jacky's books for over 25 years!

10 Thursday
DRAW IT!
Sketch your favourite scene from your favourite JW book!

DESIGN A BIRTHDAY CARD FOR NICK!

11 Friday
READ IT!
Read a book that you've given up on halfway through and not managed to finish!

12 Saturday
COLOUR IN!
Colour in some of Marigold's tattoos!

MICKY

13 Sunday

DO IT!

Paint your fingernails and toenails with a different colour or design on each one!

14 Monday

WRITE IT!

Write a story in which the main character is a compulsive liar. How will they learn that telling the truth is always the best option?

AUTHOR BIRTHDAY

15 Tuesday

E. NESBIT

Edith Nesbit, better known as E. Nesbit, was born on August 15, 1858. She wrote the book *Five Children and It*, which Jacky based her book *Four Children and It* on.

Which of Jacky's books would YOU choose to rewrite?

16 Wednesday

DRAW IT!

Look around and draw the first *orange* thing you see!

17 Thursday

WOULD YOU RATHER...

...live in Victorian times or 100 years in the future? Write a story set in the era you choose.

18 Friday

TRIVIA TIME!

Which JW book features a character called **Rhiannon**? Come up with ten character names of your own!

HAPPY BIRTHDAY

Super Coolers!

Chillax and share a summer smoothie with your besties.

You'll need a blender or hand blender to make these drinks — ask an adult to help!

EACH DRINK SERVES 4.

Berry Blast!

Whizz together

100g strawberries, raspberries or blueberries (or a mix of all three!) with 100g plain yogurt, 1 scoop of vanilla ice cream and 500ml milk.

Pour into glasses and decorate with some **whole berries.**

Peach & Banana Blitz!

Whizz together

2 peaches (peeled, stoned and chopped) with 1 banana, 100g plain, banana or peach yogurt, 1 scoop vanilla ice cream and 500ml milk.

Freeze some banana slices and float on top.

Kiwi, Lime & Coconut Crush!

Whizz together

Three peeled and **chopped kiwi** fruits, squeeze of lime juice, 100g coconut yogurt, 1 scoop of coconut ice cream and 500ml milk.

Dust kiwi slices with **caster sugar** and slide them on to the rim of each glass.

Cherries taste great in this too!

Swap the banana for 50g of raspberries or swap the peaches for 2 tsp peanut butter and 2 tsp cocoa powder!

For extra coconut taste, swap the 500ml of milk for 250ml of milk and 250ml of coconut water.

20 Sunday

How many words of three letters or more can you make out of *The Illustrated Mum*?

1–5   Uh-oh! Try some more?

6–10   Go, you! You're great with words!

11+   Wowsers! You know more words than us!

21 Monday

TRIVIA TIME!

Which JW character has a toy dog called Jumper?

Choose one of your old toys to write a story about.

22 Tuesday

Snap a silly selfie **DO IT!** and send it to the JW Mag team – our email is jwmag@dcthomson.co.uk

23 Wednesday

WRITE IT!

Imagine you are an animal. Now write a story about your life.

24 Thursday

GUESS WHO?

This character is obsessed with her favourite author and loves fairies. She has a floral-sounding name.

SKETCH YOURSELF AS A FAIRY!

LOL!

25 Friday

How do you find a member of the royal family?

Follow the foot prince!

Design a beautiful crown!

26 Saturday
DRAW IT!
Design a fabulous new pair of socks for Nick!

27 Sunday
DO IT!
Build a tent in the garden by hanging an old duvet cover over the washing line. Or if it's raining, hang it up indoors!

28 Monday
COLOUR IN!
Design an awesome new outfit for Mighty Mart!

29 Tuesday
WOULD YOU RATHER...
...bungee jump or skydive? Sketch a picture of yourself doing it!

30 Wednesday
WRITE IT!
Write an alternative ending to your favourite JW book. Flick through the pages and stop at a random place — that's your starting point!

Find Floss's fairground words!

31 Thursday

★ Toffee apple
★ Helter-skelter
★ Big wheel
★ Fortunes
★ Burger van
★ Sideshow
★ Ghost train
★ Carousel
★ Candyfloss
★ Caravan

```
I N M S R A U R H E L C
C P B I G W H E E L M A
P Z Z K T O Z W L P G N
T N U R N H U F T P I D
H W Z U O S K O E A L Y
Q N D N S E J R R E H F
K L A F U D Z T S E R L
C S S V E I T U K F Q S
A I F G A S O N E F I S
J I J A O X J E L O L S
E L T H A J A S T T H M
O K G C A G A G E E K B
N V E B U R G E R V A N
```

SUPER-FUN SEPTEMBER!

DOODLE AND DESIGN!

1 Friday

Add some jewellery around these gemstones to design some new bling for Jacky!

NAIL ART!

2 Saturday

Get a cool autumn leaf look with this neat nail art!

1. Paint your nails with autumn leaf colours. To get this effect, we took as much orange polish off the brush as possible and dragged it over our nails, then did the same again with yellow.

2. Use black polish and a toothpick to draw the veins of the leaves.

3. Finish with a touch of gold polish or glitter to add sparkle!

3 Sunday

Play a card game with your family or friends – bonus points if you learn how to play a new game!

4 Monday

Nick used to design food packaging. Design a new wrapper for your favourite sweet.

5 Tuesday

Write about what you imagine Jacky gets up to on a daily basis. What does she eat for breakfast? What is she writing about?

TRIVIA TIME!

6 Wednesday

What colour is Tilly's dress in *Rent A Bridesmaid*?

Have a go at designing your very own bridesmaid dress!

TRUTH OR DARE!

7 Thursday

TRUTH: Have you ever told a porky pie?

DARE: Say the alphabet backwards – if you can't do it, you have to sing a nursery rhyme in the style of an opera singer!

PUZZLE!

8 Friday

How long will it take you to find all these words from *Clean Break*?

Christmas ✓
Dad
Dancer ✓
Dolls
Emerald
Fairyland ✓
Jenna ✓
Maxie
Princess
Vita ✓

F	R	D	U	E	U	W	K	S	J
P	F	A	I	R	Y	L	A	N	D
T	R	E	I	X	A	M	A	A	W
S	D	I	D	S	T	P	N	E	N
Q	L	L	N	S	S	C	N	M	G
I	Z	L	I	C	E	I	E	E	A
Q	M	R	O	R	E	A	J	R	A
P	H	D	A	D	T	S	V	A	G
C	V	B	J	I	K	Q	S	L	F
F	E	Q	Y	M	Q	B	L	D	Y

9 Saturday

Check out your DVD collection and watch a film you've never seen before!

10 Sunday

Would You Rather...
...eat jelly made of mushy peas, or fish and chips with jelly on top?
Write a list of your 5 favourite foods and 5 foods you can't stand!

COLOUR IN!

11 Monday

Design a cool new onesie for Ace from *Little Darlings*!

12 Tuesday

GUESS WHO!

Her mum and dad split up at Christmas time, she has a special emerald ring and she gets to meet her favourite author, Jenna Williams.
What question would you ask your favourite author if you met them?
Write it here —

_____

_____

TRIVIA TIME!

14 Thursday

Which band from the 1970s is Jacky's all-time favourite group?
Imagine you have your own band and try writing a smash hit song.

WRITE IT!

13 Wednesday

You're staying in a holiday cottage, when one day you discover a door to a cellar you've never noticed before... What happens when you creep slowly down the creaky stairs to explore?

DRAW IT!

15 Friday

What would you look like as a JW character? Use Nick's style of drawing to sketch yourself!

MAKE THIS TRACY-TASTIC NOTEBOOK!

16 Saturday

You'll need:

- A spiral-bound notebook
- Pink paint
- A pink pencil
- A black pen
- Strips of black fabric or ribbon

1. Paint the front of your notebook pink for Tracy's face.

2. Knot strips of black fabric round the loops of the spiral. You may need to use a pencil to poke the fabric through the holes before knotting them.

3. Once you've finished Tracy's hair, add her facial features — done!

66

17 Sunday

Write a letter to Jacky and send or email it to JW Mag!

MAKE A LIST...

18 Monday

Of your top five dream holiday destinations!

DRAW IT!

TRUTH OR DARE!

20 Wednesday

TRUTH: Tell everyone about a time you got the giggles.

DARE: Go up to your friend's parents (or your own!) and say, very sincerely, "I'm having such a wonderful time!"

WRITE IT!

19 Tuesday

Do a line drawing (no colour or shading!) of your house from the outside. Try to add lots of detail to give the picture depth and texture.

21 Thursday

Write a story with the opening line:
I was just walking down the street, minding my own business – I didn't mean to get involved in a major news story...

22 Friday

Would You Rather...
...have a neck as long as a giraffe's or a nose as long as an elephant's trunk? Design and colour your own crazy creature – zebra stripes and a goldfish tail? Sounds good!

COLOUR IN!

23 Saturday

Design a decadent new outfit for Queen Tracy!

24 Sunday

Root through your wardrobe and dress up in an extravagant catwalk-worthy outfit — you'll look faaa-bulous, daaa-hling!

LOL!

25 Monday

What is Humpty Dumpty's favourite season?

Autumn - because he has a great fall!

Write a haiku (short Japanese poem) or acrostic poem about falling leaves.

DRAW IT!

26 Tuesday

Instead of writing a diary entry, draw a picture that represents your day!

DOODLE AND DESIGN!

27 Wednesday

Uh-oh, Ruby from *Double Act* has shaved off all her hair! Design some new 'dos for her!

TRUTH OR DARE!

28 Thursday

TRUTH: Have you let someone take the blame for something that you've done? Spill!

DARE: Do your best street dance moves for a minute!

WRITE IT!

29 Friday

End your story with the line: *And that was when I decided that I'd never tell a lie again....*

PERFECT APPLE PUFFS!

Sapphire shows you how to make these delicious treats!

They're as good as Mrs B's!

30 Saturday

You'll need:
1 pack of ready-made puff pastry
1 tin of apple pie filling
Sultanas (optional)
Ground cinnamon (optional)
A little milk
Flour for rolling

1. Sprinkle a little flour on your work surface and roll out the pastry till it's ½ cm thick.

2. Use a saucer as a guide to cut out circles of the pastry. Put a tablespoon of pie filling on one half of each circle.

3. If you like, you can now add some sultanas and a light sprinkle of cinnamon.

4. Brush round the outside edge with milk then flip the pastry over the top of the filling to make a half circle. Press the edges firmly together to seal and make two little slits in the top of each apple puff.

5. Brush the tops with milk then bake in the oven at 200°C for 15–20 minutes until golden and risen — ask an adult to help!

OUTSTANDING OCTOBER!

1 Sunday

Read the original version of Jacky's book *Four Children and It* – it's called *Five Children and It* and was written by E. Nesbit.

Read It!

2 Monday

Truth or Dare!

TRUTH: Have you ever accidentally called a stranger Mum?

DARE: Call the person nearest you Mum for the rest of the day!

3 Tuesday

Write down the recipe for your favourite meal so that you can share it with friends and family!

Write It!

4 Wednesday

What are the names of the triplets in *The Butterfly Club*?

Make some butterflies from paper scraps and stick them all over your room

Trivia Time!

5 Thursday

Colour in all the loot in this treasure chest!

Colour In!

6 Friday

Plan and prepare an afternoon tea to share with your friends or family tomorrow — little sandwiches and fairy cakes would be perfect!

Do It!

7 Saturday
Nail Art!

1. Paint nails a base colour. We chose a deep black shade.
2. Use a toothpick with the pointy bits cut off to dot on a contrasting shade — we chose metallic gold!
3. Finish with a top coat for extra shine!

8 Sunday

Bring back summer and design an amazing sand sculpture. Imagine if you found the Psammead when you were building it! Make a wish!

Do It!

9 Monday

Write a story with this opening line:

The trees rustled ominously in the breeze. The girls huddled closer, trying to keep warm and hidden...

Write It!

10 Tuesday

Have some 'me' time. Switch off your phone and laptop, shut your bedroom door, and do something just for you — watch your fave film, read your book, or go to bed early!

Do It!

11 Wednesday

Elsa loves making people laugh with her jokes! Make up some of your own jokes or write out a funny story and see how many smiles you get.

Write it!

12 Thursday

Design this spooky pumpkin your way!

13 Friday
Truth or Dare!

TRUTH: Tell everyone a secret ambition you have.

DARE: Do an impression of your favourite celebrity — you can only stop when someone guesses who you're pretending to be!

7 Days of Speedy Sketches!

Draw all these things Sharratt-style! Can you sketch a scene with them all in?

14 Saturday

Cupcake

15 Sunday

Daffodil

16 Monday

Jacky

17 Tuesday

Gingerbread man

18 Wednesday

Buzzy bee

19 Thursday

Kitten

20 Friday

Teddy bear

PERFECT POPCORN

21 Saturday

To make popcorn, you'll need:

- ½ cup popcorn kernels
- 1tbsp vegetable oil
- Microwavable bowl
- Microwavable plate

For a quick 'n' easy cheat, just use a bag of ready-to-pop popcorn!

- Place the popcorn in the bowl and add the oil. Toss to coat.
- Put the plate on top and cook on high for 3-4 minutes.
- Once the pops have slowed to one or two every ten seconds or so, your popcorn is cooked!
- Ask an adult to take your popcorn out of the microwave for you as the bowl will be hot and steam will escape as you lift the lid.

Always ask an adult to help in the kitchen.

fresh POPCORN

FLAVOUR STATION

Give your popcorn some pizazz with the flavour station!

Add these tasty toppings to your popcorn!

Sugar And Spice!

Melt two tsps of butter and toss the popcorn to coat. Sprinkle over sugar and cinnamon to taste.

Choco-nut!

Melt 100g of chocolate and drizzle over the popcorn along with 50g of chopped roasted peanuts.

Pancake Pop!

Melt two tsps of butter and a tbsp of maple syrup. Drizzle over the popcorn — it'll taste like hot buttered pancakes!

73

22 Sunday

Colour in this picture of April. Give her loads of funky braids!

Colour In!

23 Monday

This JW character has a number of different names – one of which was actually a number! She spends a lot of time trying to find out who she is and where she came from.

• If you could make up a new name for yourself, what would it be?

Guess Who!

24 Tuesday

Apart from cats and dogs, what is Jacky's favourite animal?

• Write a story about a wild animal showing up at your school!

Trivia Time!

25 Wednesday

Draw some ghost faces on some white plastic cups. Pop a glowstick inside to make a ghostly decoration!

Do It!

26 Thursday

Make a list...

Write down the five most exciting things that have ever happened to you!

27 Friday

Can you write a scary story about a ghost who haunts a haunted house at the funfair? Use lots of spooky descriptions to make your readers' spines tingle!

Write It!

74

ANSWERS: 23 – Hetty Feather; 24 – Lemurs

You'll need:

- Battery tealights (we used a pack of four green ones from a pound shop)
- Double-sided sticky tape
- Ribbon
- Black card
- Marker pen

WICKED WITCHES!

Eek! Make these horrible Halloween decorations for a spooky party!

1 Use the marker pen to draw an evil witch face on to each tealight — keep the eyes low to leave space for the hat.

2 Stick a strip of tape all the way round the outside edge of the tealights.

3 Cut the ribbon into pieces around 25cm long. Fold in half, then tie a knot to make a loop.

4 Place the loop at the top of each head, then stick down the ribbon all the way round the edge — trim any extra from the join under the chin.

5 Cut some witch hats from black card and decorate with ribbon scraps or metallic pens.

6 Stick the hats to the front of the tealights with little pieces of tape.

Now switch on, hang up and prepare to scare!

WHY NOT? Make some spooky ghost faces with white tealights.

29 Sunday

Design a spooky sign to hang on your door for Halloween. Stick on scary plastic spiders, pieces of tattered web and add some fake blood to make it truly frightening!

Do It!

Write It!
30 Monday

Make up a creepy Halloween poem to say while you're out Trick or Treating. Try to include all these words —

- SCREAM
- NIGHTMARE
- FRIGHT

- BEWARE
- BOO
- CREATURE

31 Tuesday

Sketch your favourite Jacqueline Wilson character in a creepy disguise — what about Jodie as a witch with Pearl as her slinky black cat?

Draw It!

I'd draw Justine as a zombie!

Eek! It's Count Tracula!

76

Hey It's November!

DO IT!

1 Wednesday

What would your dream job be when you're older? Why? Ask your family or friends to see if anyone has similar ambitions to you!

2 Thursday

TRIVIA TIME!

Which JW character lives in Bilefield?

If you could live anywhere in the world, where would you choose and why?

Write a diary entry about a day in your dream home.

3 Friday

Make a Monogram!
Sketch out your initials or your name and decorate the letters with beautiful swirls, curls and colours.

MAKE IT!

4 Saturday

Give Emerald the mermaid a beautiful new outfit!

COLOUR IN!

Answer: 2 – Destiny

Bonfire Buns!

These cute cupcakes are perfect for a fireworks party!

You'll need:

- Cupcakes
  (buy ready made or use our recipe on page 52)
- Icing
  (follow recipe on page 37, adding 1 tablespoon of cocoa powder and a splash of milk)
- Flake chocolate
- Jelly sweets

Always ask an adult for help in the kitchen!

TO DECORATE:

1 Chop up a Flake into strips like this

2 Roughly ice the cakes with chocolate icing

3 Position the Flake strips on the iced cupcake to look like a bonfire

4 Add chopped jelly sweets to look like flames — ooh!

7 Days of Writing!

I'm an A+ chatterbox!

6 Monday

Pick shuffle on your music player to choose a tune at random. Now write a story based round the song — you could describe how it makes you feel or base your tale on the words.

7 Tuesday

Awesome A Report Card!

You get the chance to create your own report card, what subjects will score the highest marks? Think about the things you're really good at and get writing!

8 Wednesday

Start a debate on the following subject –

SHOULD HOMEWORK BE BANNED?

Decide if you're for or against and write down some persuasive arguments to win your case — *it's boring* doesn't count!

9 Thursday

Pick a picture book and look carefully at the illustrations — try not to look at the words. Now see if you can write a brand new story using the drawings for inspiration!

10 Friday

TV or computer? You can only have one, so what will you choose? Write about why you made your choice.

11 Saturday

Complete a story based on this title:
The Little Boy Who Saved the World!

12 Sunday

Write a TV script for a sitcom about your family! Give each person a part to suit their personality.

13 Monday

Mind Map

Draw an outline of your head then fill it with pictures and words to show what you're thinking about right now.

14 Tuesday

DO IT!

Make up a funny rhyming song about your family: I have a dad and he is mad. My sister, Maisie, she's so crazy!

15 Wednesday

Give Marigold from *The Illustrated Mum* some fabulous new tattoos!

TRUTH OR DARE!

GUESS WHO?

16 Thursday

She has funky braided hair, she's quite shy, and she's desperate to find her birth mother after she was left outside a pizza restaurant...

Imagine you find an abandoned baby. Write a news report about it — don't forget your attention-grabbing headline!

17 Friday

TRUTH: What's something that your family or friends do that annoys you?

DARE: Do something silly to make everyone laugh — if anyone manages to keep a straight face, do something else till you have everyone in stitches!

COLOUR IN!

PUZZLE

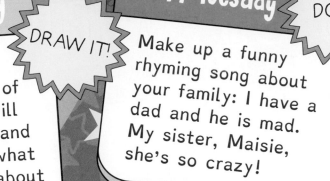

A B C D E F G H I J K L M N

O P Q R S T U V W X Y Z

18 Saturday

Use Verity's hieroglyphic code to discover her cat's name!

19 Sunday

Would You Rather...

...be able to fly OR become invisible?

Write a story based on your choice.

TRIVIA TIME!

20 Monday

Which JW book was the first one that Nick illustrated for Jacky?

Design a brand new cover for the book using all your drawing skills.

21 Tuesday

Try writing some fan fiction about your favourite celebrity — what would happen if you met them?

WRITE IT!

22 Wednesday

Grab a couple of small balls and practise juggling!

TIP!

Start by using balled-up tissues instead - they're lighter and will give you a chance to practise the technique!

DO IT!

23 Thursday

Find 10 creatures Ella from *The Longest Whale Song* might find in the sea.

PUZZLE

WHALE ✓
STARFISH ✓
OCTOPUS ✓
ANEMONE ✓
CRAB ✓

SHARK ✓
SEA URCHIN ✓
CLOWN FISH ✓
CORAL ✓
SEAHORSE ✓

L	C	L	O	W	N	F	I	S	H
S	S	A	W	H	A	L	E	E	A
U	U	T	N	C	R	A	B	A	T
G	R	P	A	T	U	W	P	H	M
W	A	O	O	R	M	U	R	O	N
D	S	X	C	T	E	G	A	R	U
U	V	H	X	M	C	I	N	S	B
F	I	K	A	C	B	O	S	E	A
N	V	C	O	R	A	L	R	H	E
J	W	V	C	P	K	H	C	V	Z

24 Friday

Try out this super-easy nail look!

1. Paint your nails a base colour — we went for red!
2. Use the pointed end of a toothpick to dot on a contrasting colour.
3. Continue adding more colours till your nails are mesmerizingly multi-coloured! Finish with a clear top coat!

NAIL ART!

1 2 3

Firework Art!

You'll need:
- Card
- Wax crayons
- Black poster paint
- A paintbrush

This technique is super-effective for creating a colourful fireworks scene!

1 Colour a sheet of card using wax crayons in a range of bright colours, like this.

2 Paint over the top of the card with black poster paint to create your night sky. You may need to apply two or more coats to cover the wax crayon completely.

3 Once dry, take the end of a paintbrush and gently scratch away to create all sorts of different fireworks. The colourful wax crayon will shine through, contrasting with the black!

26 Sunday

Write down your three biggest wishes! Why did you choose these things?

MAKE A LIST...

27 Monday

DO IT!

Make a new friend at school. Be brave and speak to someone you haven't talked to before. Start with a smile and a compliment such as I like your bag or hair or shoes, and see where it goes from there!

28 Tuesday

DOODLE AND DESIGN!

Design a glamorous new necklace for Jacky!

29 Wednesday

AUTHOR BIRTHDAY

LOUISA M. ALCOTT

Louisa May Alcott was born on November 29, 1832 in Pennsylvania, USA. She wrote the book *Little Women*, which is one of Jacky's favourites, and also its sequels *Little Men* and *Jo's Boys*.

Which of Jacky's books would you like her to write a sequel for? What do you think would happen to the characters in your favourite JW book if the story continued?

30 Thursday

DRAW IT!

Ask a family member to describe someone they know that you've never met — try to draw them and see how accurate you are!

DELIGHTFUL DECEMBER!

READ IT!

1 Friday

How many books will you manage to read this month? One, two... ten? Set yourself the challenge and see if you can do it!

PUZZLE!

3 Sunday

Can you find all these words relating to Jacky's autobiography *My Secret Diary*?

Chris ✓   Kingston ✓
Cookie ✓   Latchmere ✓
Coombe ✓   Records ✓
Dancing ✓   School ✓
Diary ✓   Writing ✓

S	Z	C	S	C	P	L	G	H	L
U	D	O	Z	R	O	N	Z	A	H
S	I	R	H	C	I	O	T	I	I
G	B	C	O	T	Y	C	K	B	Y
N	C	O	I	C	H	R	S	I	Y
I	J	R	N	M	E	C	A	I	E
C	W	V	E	Q	H	R	K	I	Z
N	I	R	C	O	O	M	B	E	D
A	E	N	O	T	S	G	N	I	K
D	Z	L	A	L	H	I	S	L	B

2 Saturday

Would You Rather...

...have to sing your favourite song really loudly every time you walked into a room for a week **OR** wear your pyjamas to school for a week?

Design some lovely new pjs for yourself — you might be wearing them a lot!

TRIVIA TIME!

4 Monday

How many JW books does Tracy Beaker appear in?

What would happen if Tracy met Justine when they've grown up? Will they still be enemies, or could they ever be friends? Write a new chapter of Tracy's story.

5 Tuesday

"I never said he stole my sweets" – depending on which word you emphasise, this sentence can have lots of different meanings. "I never said *he* stole my sweets" is different from "I never said he stole my *sweets*".
Choose one word to stress and write a story about what happens!

6 Wednesday

TRUTH: Has a JW book ever made you cry? If so, which one?
DARE: Stand outside and sing *I Wish It Could Be Christmas Every Day* in your silliest voice!

7 Thursday

Create a snowy winter scene using only finger-painting – no brushes allowed!

8 Friday

Use words and letters cut out from magazines or newspapers to create a sign for your bedroom door!

9 Saturday

How many hula hoops can you spin at once? Challenge your besties to see who's the most skilled spinner!

Can you beat Jacky?

HOOP, HOOP HURRAY!

Answers:
4 – The Story Of Tracy Beaker, The Dare Game, Starring Tracy Beaker and Tracy Beaker's Thumping Heart.

85

WE ♡ FUDGE!

10 Sunday

You'll need:

- 500g caster sugar
- 400g condensed milk
- 100g butter

Make yummy fudge in the microwave!

1. Put the butter, milk and sugar in a large microwave-proof bowl.

2. Microwave on high power for two and a half minutes or till butter has melted. Stir the ingredients together.

3. Microwave on high power for 10 minutes, stirring every minute or so. Keep an eye on the mixture and pause cooking if it looks like it's going to bubble over.

Always ask an adult for help in the kitchen!

4. After 10 minutes, remove from the microwave and pour into a greased tin. Leave to cool and cut into squares!

Be careful when touching the bowl — it will be hot!

MIX IT UP!

Try these awesome flavour additions!

PEANUT BUTTER BITE!
Add a tablespoon of peanut butter at the start.

NICE 'N' NUTTY
Add a tablespoon of Nutella to the mix. You could also add a handful of chopped nuts to the fudge as well!

PEPPERMINT DREAM
Add a few drops of peppermint extract to the fudge after it's finished cooking. You could also crush some candy canes and sprinkle over the top before the fudge sets!

11 Monday

Would You Rather...

...only eat your favourite food for ever and ever or eat a **BIG** piece of Christmas cake smothered in gravy and cranberry sauce once.

Design a beautiful cake with a snowy icing scene on top.

PUZZLE!

12 Tuesday

Solve this riddle to find where Hetty and Diamond take their stage show in *Little Stars*.

My first is in **TOP** but not in **HOP**.

My second is in **HAT** but not in **BAT**.

My third is the last in **THREE**.

My fourth and ninth are the first in **CAT**.

My fifth, seventh and tenth are the middle in **HAT**.

My sixth is in **VENT** but not in **TENT**.

My eighth is the first in **LEAN**.

My eleventh is in **DENT** but not in **BENT**.

My last is the last in **BEE**.

GUESS WHO?

13 Wednesday

He's fun and friendly and has a name that he shares with a yummy treat!

Which other JW character could he be good friends with? Choose a good match for him and write them into a new adventure.

WRITE IT!

14 Thursday

Make up five new words and include them in a story about aliens landing on Earth!

COLOUR IN!

15 Friday

Add some colour to this peacock — will you use beautiful blues and greens or go for a rainbow of different shades?

DRAW IT!

16 Saturday

Give Tracy Beaker a Christmas party makeover and draw the results!

HAPPY BIRTHDAY JACKY!

WRITE IT!

17 Sunday

Jacky was born on December 17, 1945.

She's written over 100 books and is one of the best-loved children's authors of all time!

Write down your favourite thing about Jacky.

18 Monday

Write a story about your dream Christmas! Will it be full of lavish gifts and fabulous food, or will you wish for fun, friends and family?

PUZZLE!

19 Tuesday

Crack the code to reveal which JW book starts on Christmas Day.

C L E A N

B R E A K

20 Wednesday

Would You Rather...

...be able to read other people's minds or see into the future?

Write a list of things you'd like to happen in 2018 and put it in a safe place. Check on this day next year to see how many have come true!

SYMBOL KEY

A= B= C= D= E= F= G=
H= I= J= K= L= M= N=
O= P= Q= R= S= T= U=
V= W= X= Y= Z=

LOL!

21 Thursday

What do you get when you eat Christmas decorations? Tinsellitus!

Make your own crackers and fill them with hilarious jokes you've made up!

COLOUR IN!

22 Friday

Colour in this picture of Jacky as a teenager! Will you give her a sparkly new outfit so that she's ready for a Christmas party?

PRIMP UP YOUR PRESENTS!

23 Saturday

You'll need:
- Plain paper
(we used white and brown)
- Marker pens
- Craft tape scraps

Impress your friends and family with amazing gift wrap — it's so easy!

Use the plain paper to wrap your boxes then copy these pictures and tips to create fab designs!

DRAW ON CUTE FACES!

Cat 'n' Mouse Cuties
- Leave these tabs unstuck and draw on the cat ears.
- Cut some mouse ears and stick to the front of the box.
- Tape on twine tails!

Bow-tiful!
Criss-cross tape strips for this gorgeous bow effect.

Polar Pal
Cut some little bear ears and paws and tape or glue them on. Aww!

Tape Tree
Finish with some stick-on gem baubles!

Stick & Sketch!
Use your marker pens to turn tape strips into candles or a pretty parcel.

AUTHOR BIRTHDAY

Noel Streatfeild

Noel was born in England on Christmas Eve 1895. She wrote many children's books including one of Jacky's favourites, *Ballet Shoes*. Just like Jacky, some of her books were turned into TV shows and films.

25 Monday

It's Christmas! Make a List...

Of all the best things that have happened to you today!

DO IT!

24 Sunday

Which of Jacky's books would you like to see on TV? Write an outline with all your reasons – could you persuade a film producer to adapt it for screen?

OPAL'S ACTIVITY FINDER

26 Tuesday

Play an old-fashioned game with your friends. Try hopscotch, skipping or hide-and-seek if it's not too cold. If it's raining play tiddlywinks or ludo. What other old-fashioned games can you think of?

DO IT!

27 Wednesday

Have a crazy tidying up day! Organise your books alphabetically and sort out your wardrobe by colour. Give anything you don't need to charity. You'll get lots of extra Brownie points for it *and* you'll be able to find all your stuff!

WRITE IT!

28 Thursday

You get sucked into your favourite video game – how do you survive when someone starts trying to control you?

DO IT!

29 Friday

Interview a grandparent or older relative to find out how different life was when they were your age!

ULTIMATE ART CHALLENGE!

30 Saturday

Can you create something arty every day for a whole year? Grab some plain postcards and do a sketch, design or painting. Use the address side to record the date and details of each creation. Check back next year to see how you did!

MAKE A LIST...

31 Sunday

Write down your hopes and dreams for 2018!

The Sharratt Files

So Nick, let's find out all about you and the life of an artist extraordinaire —

What does your studio look like?

It's a bit messy, I'm afraid. I have all the books I've ever worked on, my trusty computer, hundreds of pens and pencils and paints, and lots of sketches and artwork. My shop model, Joan, keeps me company when I work — and I always wear my special artist slippers!

You draw a lot — almost as much as I talk! Do you ever get tired of drawing?

No, I never get tired of drawing, but I do like a break from it at weekends. On the other hand, if I have more than a week away from the drawing board, I begin to worry that I might forget how to do it!

What would you do if you weren't an artist?

If I weren't able to be involved in art and design in some way, I think I'd have to go back to the only other job I've ever really had — delivering newspapers.

What's the thing you've most loved drawing? (Hint, hint, hint — me, me, me!).

You ARE my favourite character to draw, actually. But I really enjoy drawing animals in my picture books too — elephants, lions and giraffes especially.

Obviously I've never experienced any Lapses in Creativity, but do you ever get artist's block?

I can't afford to get artist's block! A professional illustrator is always up against a deadline — the time when a job has to be completed and handed in, and there's nothing like a deadline to get the brain cells working, I can tell you.

Which character do you find easiest to draw?

Well, funny you should ask — it's you!

Who is the hardest?

Teenage boys in general always involve a bit of head-scratching — how do I make their faces not too young — but at the same time not too mature? And how do I style their hair to make them look up-to-date?

Have you and Jacky ever had A Heated Discussion about the vision of a character?

No! Once or twice I might have suggested a change of hairstyle or a different kind of school uniform and Jacky has always been really accommodating.

Do you have any little quirky things you have to do before you start drawing? Maybe lining up all your pencils then twirling three times before you sit down?

I have to know exactly where my scalpel is. I use one to sharpen my pencils, instead of a pencil sharpener, and I am ALWAYS losing it, so that is more or less a daily ritual.

Art materials have become extremely scarce. You can only choose ONE of these. Which do you pick and why?

- One single black felt pen
- A box of six plain graphite pencils
- Three tubes of paint in red, blue and yellow

Black felt pen — there's something about a clean, smooth, properly black line that I loved as a boy and I still love. I HATE it, however, when felts begin to run out and the ink is not a perfect black.

What are your favourite pens and pencils to use?

When I'm drawing in public I like quite chunky black felt pens. For some book illustrations I use a technical pen called a Rotring, with a 0.5 nib. For the majority of my picture book work and the covers of Jacky's books I use a 6B pencil, and add the colour digitally.

What do you do when you're not drawing, Nick? Any hobbies?

Snoozing and napping and having forty winks — at which I am a real master!

If you were appearing on *Celebrity Come Dine with Me*, which four celebs would you like take part with?

Sir David Attenborough, Sir Paul McCartney, Meryl Streep and Nigella Lawson please.

What's on your menu?

I'd probably make egg and chips, that's my speciality. And lots of cake. And strawberry milkshake. And some sweets, I *love* sweets... A posh prawn cocktail, pasta with homemade pesto sauce and a really good trifle for pud, all of which aren't too hard to make.

Which celebrity reality show would you like to appear on?

Strictly Come Dancing. Maybe Jacky could be my partner?